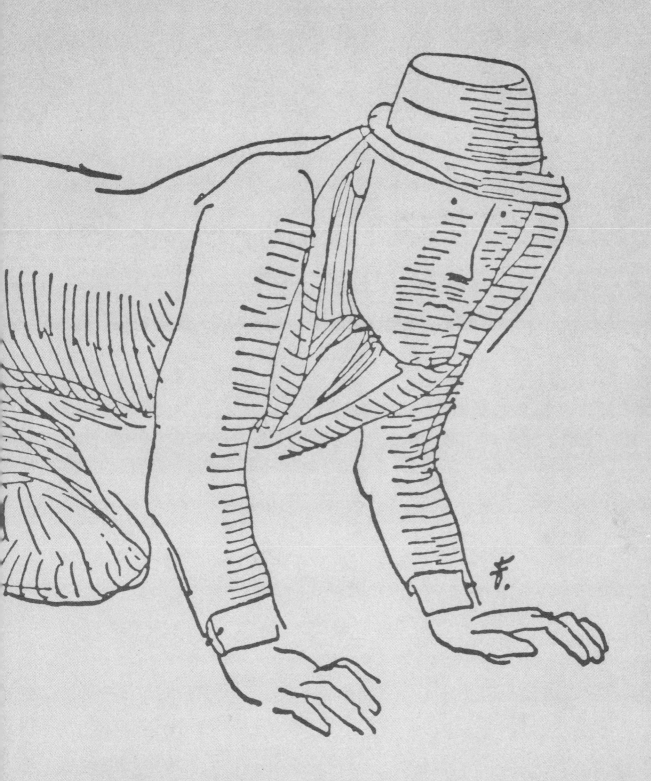

FEIFFER'S

Random House / New York

aLBUM

Jules Feiffer

Books by Jules Feiffer:

Sick, Sick, Sick
Passionella and Other Stories
The Explainers
Boy, Girl. Boy, Girl.
Hold Me, Hold Me
The Feiffer Album

First Printing

© Copyright, 1958, 1961, 1963, by Jules Feiffer
© Copyright, 1962, 1963, by The Curtis Publishing Company
© Copyright, 1962, 1963, by HMH Publishing Co., Inc.
All rights reserved under International and Pan-American Copyright
Conventions. Published in New York by Random House, Inc., and
simultaneously in Toronto, Canada, by Random House of Canada, Limited.

Library of Congress Catalog Card Number: 63-8335

Manufactured in the United States of America

TABLE OF CONTENTS

To My Parents

Introduction

The scene is the darkened stage of a Broadway playhouse. A spot comes up on the FIRST SATIRIST, *who is seated on a stool reading a newspaper. A second spot comes up on the* SECOND SATIRIST, *who is staring at him.*

SECOND SATIRIST   Are you a satirist?

FIRST SATIRIST   Can't you tell?

SECOND SATIRIST   Well, you *are* sitting on a stool.

FIRST SATIRIST   Want to hear my Kennedy bit?

SECOND SATIRIST (*Winces*)   I must have the wrong place. I heard there were going to be some satirists here.

FIRST SATIRIST (*Offended*)   I *am* a satirist.
  (*A spot comes up on the* THIRD SATIRIST)

THIRD SATIRIST   So am I.

SECOND SATIRIST   Where's your stool?

THIRD SATIRIST   I'm a right-wing satirist. Only liberal satirists have stools. We right-wing satirists have to be ready to make a fast start.

FIRST SATIRIST   You right-wingers! You always make yourselves sound so oppressed. Now take me! *I'm* not strictly a liberal. Did you ever hear me do Kennedy?

THIRD SATIRIST   I've heard everybody do Kennedy.

FIRST SATIRIST   Proves my point. I do a very strong Kennedy.

THIRD SATIRIST Ever been invited to the White House?

FIRST SATIRIST Every time I do Kennedy.

SECOND SATIRIST I don't think either one of you knows what satire is—
  (*A spot comes up on the* FOURTH SATIRIST)

FOURTH SATIRIST It's Jewish, isn't it? Lots of words like *schtick, l'chaim, bagel.* That's what I use in *my* act.
  (*A spot comes up on the* FIFTH SATIRIST—*a Negro*)

FIFTH SATIRIST Jewish is square, man. The roots of modern-day satire rest in the jazz idiom. Satire has crossed the color line.

FOURTH SATIRIST (*Smiles indulgently at the* FIFTH SATIRIST) Oh, don't get me wrong.

THIRD SATIRIST (*Smiles indulgently at the* FIFTH SATIRIST) Don't get me wrong.

FIRST SATIRIST (*Smiles indulgently*) Don't get me wrong, either. I do a great Kennedy on the phone to Martin Luther King.

FIFTH SATIRIST Martin Luther King? Man, as far as *my* audience goes, Martin Luther King is practically *white!*

FIRST SATIRIST (*Nervously to the audience*) We're all just kidding here. Having fun. That's what satire is. Having fun.

SECOND SATIRIST Do you always apologize?

FIRST SATIRIST A satirist can't teach people anything if he offends them.

FOURTH SATIRIST I offend them. They love it. I make fun of their wives. They love it. I tell them I hate them. They love it. I use words like *schmuck.* You should hear them applaud.

THIRD SATIRIST I like to work with my audience. I like to improvise. I ask them to give me a first line and a last line and a theme. And I build a whole fifteen-minute improvisation around it.

FIFTH SATIRIST Is it any good?

THIRD SATIRIST Never. But they love it. I ingratiate myself.

SECOND SATIRIST That's not satire. All you want is approval.

THIRD SATIRIST Yes. And when they withhold it, I attack them.

FOURTH SATIRIST Me, too. Viciously.

FIFTH SATIRIST Man, I don't want approval.

THE OTHERS (*Approvingly*) What do you want?

FIFTH SATIRIST Yo' sister! (*The others recoil*) That was satire.

FIRST SATIRIST Hey, I can do a great Kennedy. (*Thrusts out forefinger*) Do naht ahsk what you can do fer Caroline—

FOURTH SATIRIST (*Impatient*) Everyone does Kennedy. That's not satire. Now the kind of satire *I* like to do—

2

FIRST SATIRIST   Kennedy is so satire. He's the President, isn't he? When you do the President you're making fun of a public figure, aren't you? You're making him look foolish, aren't you? That takes courage, doesn't it? Well, when I do Kennedy that's satire! Unabashed, unafraid satire.

FIFTH SATIRIST   Do J. Edgar Hoover.

FIRST SATIRIST   J. Edgar Hoover?

FIFTH SATIRIST   Do J. Edgar Hoover.

FIRST SATIRIST   You don't want J. Edgar Hoover.

FIFTH SATIRIST   Man, I'm *colored*. It ain't my F.B.I. Do J. Edgar Hoover. (FIRST SATIRIST *backs off*) You said you do public figures.

FIRST SATIRIST   Yeah, but J. Edgar Hoover. I mean—listen, if you come to my house and we close all the windows—

FIFTH SATIRIST   Do it here—now.

FIRST SATIRIST   I do a *great* Kennedy.

FIFTH SATIRIST   J. Edgar Hoover.

FIRST SATIRIST   On a stage? In front of people? It's bad taste! Let me do the President!
(FIFTH SATIRIST *scornfully turns away*)

FOURTH SATIRIST   The kind of satire I prefer to do is the take-off on the little man—

SECOND SATIRIST   Dear God!

FOURTH SATIRIST   His troubles, his pet peeves.

SECOND SATIRIST   Heaven help us!

FOURTH SATIRIST   The little unnoticed bedevilments of life that may not give the audience a belly laugh, mind you, but will give them a smile of recognition. "Yes—I'm like that," they'll say. "There I am. There you are. There we all are. Little Man. Peering off into the middle distance."

SECOND SATIRIST   I'm ill.

FOURTH SATIRIST   "There's my wife. There's my next door neighbor—"

SECOND SATIRIST   Together?

FOURTH SATIRIST   (*Self-righteous*)   Smut is *not* satire.

SECOND SATIRIST   Smut, dear sir, is our *only* satire.

FOURTH SATIRIST   You're one of those people who has to attack everything!

FIFTH SATIRIST   (*To* SECOND SATIRIST)   You ain't ever attacked *me*, baby.

SECOND SATIRIST   Of course not. Now is not the *time* to attack you. When you've gained equal rights —*then* I'll attack you.

FIRST SATIRIST   (*Proudly*)   *I* have a point of view. *I* don't attack everything.

FOURTH SATIRIST   (*Proudly*)   Certainly! One should be *for* something. Then he can attack those things that are against what he is for. That's the *responsible* approach.

FIFTH SATIRIST   You for something?

FIRST SATIRIST *(With inspiration)*   Everybody's for something.

FIFTH SATIRIST   What're you for?

FIRST SATIRIST *(With inspiration)*   Compassion!

THIRD SATIRIST *(With inspiration)*   Understanding!

FOURTH SATIRIST *(With inspiration)*   Love!
(*All three shake hands*)

SECOND SATIRIST *(To* FIFTH SATIRIST*)*   And you—what are you for?

FIFTH SATIRIST   Man, I don't stand for nothin'. I'm just a little old plantation hand doing his bit to make the system work. A civil rights therapist to lily-white audiences.

SECOND SATIRIST *(Exultant)*   You *shame* them! You *expose* them!

FIFTH SATIRIST   I make them laugh. They relax. They feel very liberal. Then they put on their sheets and go home. That's what satire is, man. Communication.

FIRST SATIRIST *(Shaking hands with* FIFTH SATIRIST*)*   A very interesting statement. Satire *is* communication.

FOURTH SATIRIST *(Shaking hands with* FIFTH SATIRIST*)*   Communication! Extremely well put.

THIRD SATIRIST *(Shaking hands with* FIFTH SATIRIST*)*   Communication. Well said. Where did you go to school?

SECOND SATIRIST *(Angry)*   Satire is *not* concerned with communication! Satire is concerned with *hate!*

FIRST SATIRIST *(Sweetly)*   Yes, but hate is the satirist's bridge to communication!

THIRD SATIRIST *(Sweetly)*   Satire should *never* be negative. Hate is only a device.

SECOND SATIRIST *(Furious)*   Satire outrages! Satire strips bare!

FIRST SATIRIST   I outrage.

THIRD SATIRIST   I strip bare.

SECOND SATIRIST *(Screams)*   Satire exposes our inner corruption! Satire *destroys!*

FOURTH SATIRIST *(Defensively)*   Well I'm sure we *all* want to destroy. *(Brightly)* But only in order to build.

FIRST SATIRIST   Yes! That's the only reason we'd ever destroy. To build on the ashes.

THIRD SATIRIST   *A better society!*

FOURTH SATIRIST   *A saner tomorrow!*

FIRST SATIRIST   *An improved image of man!*

FIFTH SATIRIST   *A happy people—with a natural sense of rhythm!*

FIRST, THIRD and FOURTH SATIRISTS *(Sing)*   Hallelujah!
(*All four shake hands*)

THIRD SATIRIST   Don't you see? That's the whole *point* in destroying. That's why satire is *not* negative!

4

FOURTH SATIRIST   That's why it's healthy!

SECOND SATIRIST *(Becoming convinced)*   I see! Yes!

FOURTH SATIRIST   Not really sadistic at all!

SECOND SATIRIST *(With inspiration)*   Yes!

FIRST SATIRIST   It builds on ashes.

SECOND SATIRIST   Yes! Ashes, we need ashes!

THIRD SATIRIST   On which to build!
  (He lights a match)

ALL   Ashes! *(They each light a match)   Ashes!*
  (They set fire to the curtains. The Theatre begins to burn—scenery, backdrops, etc.)

FIRST SATIRIST   Very soon now we will start to build.
  (All shake hands as the theatre goes up in flames)

EXCALIBUR AND ROSE

There was once a funny, awkward little man named Excalibur, who made his living entertaining the villagers in the township where he lived. He sang. He danced. He recited parables to fit the time. It was said that there was no dispute Excalibur could not settle by gathering before him the disputants and mocking them gently till their self-righteous frowns changed to embarrassed grins and their bitter quarrel seemed only a trifle.

But though he was loved by all and though he loved all without exception, Excalibur felt a longing—for what reason he could not tell. "Perhaps mine is but a longing to have a longing," he joked to himself, attempting to make as little of his problem as he did of everyone else's. But each joke drove the longing deeper until he, at last, was forced to seek out Father Know-It-All, the wisest man in the village.

"Your longing is to be two-sided," said Father Know-It-All, forcibly restraining a smile as Excalibur tried to amuse him by executing a series of head and hand stands. "At the moment you are one-sided. You are all *happiness*. You must cultivate a *serious* side. You must practice to be happy when happiness is called for and to be serious when seriousness is called for. Then you will be a two-sided person and your longing will disappear."

And so it was that early the next morning Excalibur rode quietly from his village, softly singing farewell to the sleeping things he loved—and, more loudly, singing hello to the new world he was about to enter in search of his serious side.

During his first night's encampment he was awakened by the sound of sighing. "Sad, sad, sad," said a tragic voice. "All is sad, sad, sad." Near the dying coals of his fire there stood the gravest, yet lovliest girl he had ever seen. "Do not look upon me," warned the girl, "for so grave a disposition have I, that all those who gaze upon this, my face, are immediately consumed by grief and tears."

Excalibur bounded happily from his bedroll. "All those who look upon *my* face cannot help but laugh at the simple joys of living!" And to prove his point he broke into a remarkable dance, reciting as he turned cartwheels his entire repertoire of songs and sayings. But the girl sighed only the louder for it saddened her to know that such a gay young man would, at any moment, be consumed by grief and tears.

Hours later, with one exhausted by entertaining and the other debilitated by sighing, they fell in a state of collapse—chuckling and weeping in their respective slumbers.

The next morning the girl told her story. "My name is Rose. All my life I have sought the perfection implicit in that name—for what is more perfect than a rose? But feeling deeply the imperfections in myself and those around me, I grew moody and sullen. Each year and each experience taught me more clearly just how hideously imperfect the world had become, even to the point of infecting with its faults the lives of those nearest and dearest to me—my own beloved parents. With industry and patience I tried to correct these faults, but in my eagerness to help I only hindered. My parents took my advice unkindly and referred to me as a grouch and a long-face. It was then that I took to sighing, following them about and asking plaintively, 'Am I such a terrible person for wanting to improve you? Have I ever asked you to do anything that was wrong?' They began to throw sticks at me.

"One morning I awoke to find a note pinned to their unslept-in bed. Mother and Father had run away! The note explained that their only desire was for me to find happiness and if I ever succeeded I must send for them. But I know I cannot find happiness until I find perfection. So that is my quest: I shall hunt the land till I flush it out, wherever it may hide."

Excalibur was enthralled by the excitement of Rose's quest and asked if he might join her, for he hoped that by applying all his powers of observation he might successfully learn to imitate her seriousness. While en route he told Rose his own story. "When I was born, my mother, a good but slightly addled woman, fancied that I was not my father's son but the kidnapped child of some legendary king whose exploits she had heard and thrilled to in her childhood, and whose kingdom she much preferred I inherit than the accumulated debts of my *real* father. It was for this king that she determined to name me, but being heir to a faulty memory (which my father, under the circumstances, had no desire to correct) she gave me the name "Excalibur," who she remembered ruled a great kingdom aided only by the power of his trusty, well-tempered sword Arthur. The subsequent pattern of my life has followed closely the logic of my christening."

One day, intent upon their quest, Excalibur and Rose rode into a strange village whose busy market place was crowded for its great length of stalls with hordes of pressing, pushing, expressionless people. "It may be wisest to search first among the poor," said Rose, "for the rich, having small need to work, own more time to court temptation and thereby encourage imperfection." Excalibur agreed.

Cheerfully he cried out, "Who among you is so poor that he lives in perfection?" But though he repeated the question in many funny voices he could not divert a single eye from the merchandise. "We are in a world geared to trade," explained Excalibur. "Nothing here is considered of value unless it is marked with a price."

"How sad," said Rose, and she wept.

"How hilarious," said Excalibur. He thereupon found a loose board on which he painted the words, *"Tears for Sale"*; and placing the sign on an empty stall, he sat Rose on a stool directly under it. "Here in the market place no one laughs and no one weeps," said Excalibur. "They are too busy to have feelings and too active to have emotions. But if we disguise ourselves as marketable, we may yet be heard." Then in a loud voice he cried, "Tears for sale! Buy your river of flowing tears!"

A crowd formed in no time. It pressed in closely, cautiously inspecting the new product for merits and defects. Coins began to be tossed into Rose's lap. Handkerchiefs fought battles beneath her chin to see whose would catch the biggest tear. Through it all Rose sat, singing sadly of a people grown so imperfect that in order to have tears they must purchase them. At the end of the song her audience was shaking with sobs.

Tears spread like a contagion and within moments the market place was immersed—a sight that brought the happiest of grins to Excalibur's face. Thrilled with Rose's accomplishment, he leaped to the roof of the stall and danced for joy.

The irresistibility of his mood soon cracked the spell of weeping, and the crowd, confused by this sudden onslaught of emotions, lapsed into an uncontrollable fit of the giggles. And so the day wore on—first with Rose and the crowd weeping, then with Excalibur and the crowd dancing for joy. By nightfall the exhausted village had made heroes of the two young people: Excalibur, for his genius to inspire laughter, and Rose, for her knowledge of the soul.

Now such a remarkable change in the life of a town could not long go unnoticed by the paternal eye of the King—Kind Wicked III, who for years had brooded over the bored reaction of his people to the profitable subject of war. He dispatched four of his most trusted counselors to fetch these curious travelers who might be of use to him. But at their first sight of Rose and Excalibur, the counselors wept and laughed to such a degree that they forgot completely the purpose of their mission, resigned from the king's services and, from that day, traveled the land as monks.

Only by himself accosting them in the black of night where even a star was forbidden to flicker was the king able to complete his mission, bringing to his palace in masks and chains the happy man and the serious girl. Once there, he banished Excalibur to the dungeons as his hostage, and had sad Rose brought before him, crying softly into her mask which the king forbade her to remove lest he too be reduced to tears.

King Kind Wicked III explained, "My family history has been a proud one of triumph and acquisition. My father's father, King Kind Wicked I, led a gallant and vengeful people to victory after victory until the one crushing defeat that ended his life. My father, King Kind Wicked II, led a noble and vindictive people to victory after victory until the one crushing defeat that ended *his* life. I, King Kind Wicked III, have been the only monarch in our history thus far unable to undertake a single act of war. My exhortations fall on listless ears. I cannot raise money for battle, because people hoard it for trade. I cannot make our youths into warriors, because they would rather bargain than be brave. My people have forgotten the enemy's name—but still I must arouse them to anger. Anger can only follow shame and shame can only follow tears. It is through the mechanics of weeping that I will manufacture the spirit of heroism in battle."

And so with the forced consent of Rose the King set off on a speech-making tour of the provinces—and wherever he spoke, there by his side stood Rose weeping sadly. Her sorrow blanketed the land, leaving a void of despair which the King quickly filled with his talk of war. He sent out a cry to right the outrages that had driven his kingdom to tears; and the kingdom, feeling rage growing out of its tears of shame, responded vigorously.

None of this was known to Excalibur, who languished happily in his dungeon refreshing his spirits with the amusing nonsense he imagined in the shadows. His guards, though ordered not to, could not resist peering in to discover what secret joy there was to be found in a darkened cell. And once having looked they had to laugh, and having laughed they had to slide free the bolt from the iron door and lead Excalibur

into the prison yard, where he was ordered to dance for them. And when Excalibur danced *they* had to dance, joining hands while kicking their way merrily around the walls of the prison till there was not a guard or official not so taken with the joy of the occasion that he was able to remember the next day just when the prisoner slipped off into the darkness.

On the eve before the King was to make his public declaration of war, he was gathered with his speech writers to decide a difficult question of phraseology, there being a furious debate over whether the term "peace" should properly precede or follow the term "freedom-loving."

Quickly scurrying past the King's guard, Excalibur followed the sound of sighing to Rose's tent, where the two friends were at last back together, laughing and crying: she, filled with tales of horror about her journey, he, interrupting with airy tidbits from the dungeon. Finally Rose could stand no more of it. Bitterly she pushed Excalibur away from her and decried his one-sidedness as incorrigible. She could no longer suffer idiocy disguised as happiness. She flung open the flap of her tent and ordered Excalibur to leave. But he did not leave. He could not. Instead, to the astonishment of both, he fell at her feet and wept. And speaking through his first set of tears, he said, "Let me stay. I love you." And Rose, seeing his tears through tears of her own, knew that she loved him as well.

They embraced as lovers, and the longing Excalibur had felt these many months was gone, replaced now with a fullness of soul he had never known before. "Oh, my dear Rose, I have found my serious side. It is *you!*" And he wept with great satisfaction, and Rose wept with him. Then Excalibur looked beyond his own tears and noted that in the midst of her gleaming wet face, Rose wore a smile.

"I have never enjoyed weeping before," Rose explained. "It is different to weep in the company of one you care for." And the lovers embraced once again.

With a soberness that was new to him Excalibur outlined a plan. "Tomorrow when the king speaks you will not cry."

"But I always cry," said Rose.

"You must laugh. Look only at me in the crowd. I will make you laugh."

Rose cried, "I have never laughed. The best I am able to do is smile through tears." But Excalibur reassured her and, with a parting embrace, disappeared into the night.

The next morning a nervous crowd gathered in the village square to hear the King's declaration. The King appeared with Rose beside him, her teeth firmly clenched to hold back the tears. As the King began to speak Rose's eyes searched the crowd for Excalibur, only to find him just below her, waving wildly while twisting his face into a maze of silly expressions. Rose looked dumbly at him—and began to cry. Excalibur crossed his eyes, wiggled his ears, blew out his cheeks and stuck out his tongue till it touched his nose. Rose wept louder. The crowd wept with her and Excalibur, struck by the helpless look on the face of his beloved, began to weep too. And suddenly Rose smiled. The tears ran down the furiously mugging face of Excalibur, and Rose just beamed at him, warming the crowd with her smile till the King, sensing the sharp change of mood, stammered in the midst of his speech and came to a halt. But Rose did not notice. Her eyes saw only Excalibur, who earnestly redoubled his efforts at ear-wiggling, eye-crossing and tongue-stretching—crying helplessly all the while. Rose

descended from the balcony and the crowd parted for her. She took Excalibur's face in her hands and smiled into it. "At this moment I have found my perfection." She patted his face, gently drying the tears, and as they faded from his eyes Excalibur grinned. And Rose laughed. And the people, not understanding a thing of what they saw, broke into cheers, leaving little for the King to do but tear up his speech and stalk off.

Excalibur brought Rose home to his village, where together they built a house of eight sides: one side for happiness, one side for seriousness and six spare sides to contain what new knowledge of themselves and the world their future together might bring.

The End

Harold Swerg

could hit a baseball farther than any man alive —

could —

KICK a football farther than any man alive –

could –

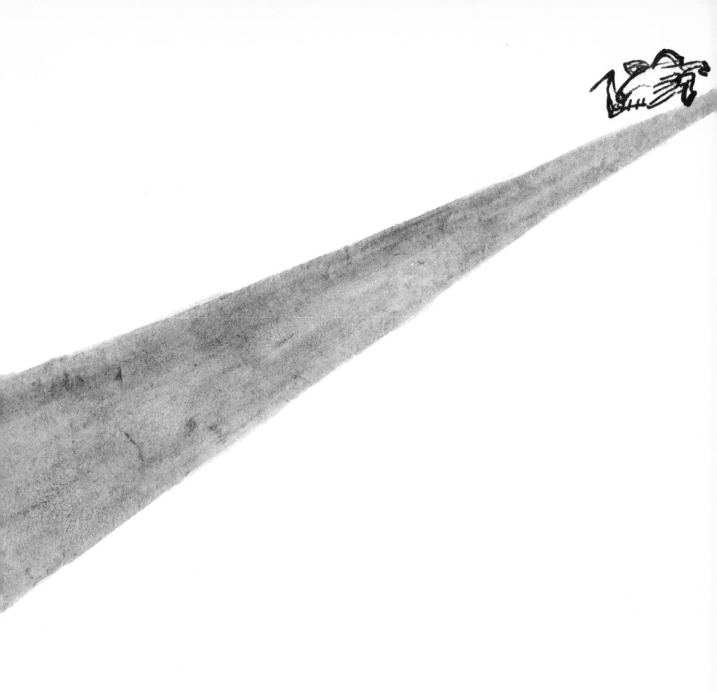

run the mile faster than any man alive.

Harold Swerg could do anything

Only he wouldn't.

Baseball and football magnates came to Harold Swerg. They said:

SIGN WITH US! YOU'LL HAVE MONEY, STATUS, GLORY GIRLS!

Track and field magnates came to Harold Swerg. They said:

SIGN WITH US! YOU'LL HAVE FREE TRANSPORT- ATION, LOTS OF BANQUETS, A TEAM JACKET WITH YOUR NAME ON IT, GIRLS!

And to all of them Harold Swerg replied:

He just wanted to go on making his living as a filing clerk.

I DON'T **LIKE** THE SPORT BUSINESS. I **LIKE** THE FILING CLERK BUSINESS.

THE SPORT BUSINESS DOESN'T PRESENT A CHALLENGE. THE FILING CLERK BUSINESS PRESENTS A CHALLENGE.

SOMEDAY I **MAY**
MAKE BOOK KEEPER.

So the baseball magnates and the football magnates and the track and field magnates all got together and issued a press release.

And people read it and said:

OBVIOUSLY ANY MAN WHO DOES NOT PLAY THE GAME IS **AGAINST** THE GAME AND IF HE IS AGAINST THE GAME HE IS AGAINST **FAIR PLAY** AND IF HE IS AGAINST FAIR PLAY HE IS AGAINST **OUR WAY OF LIFE!**

BOO!

To all of which Harold Swerg replied:

LEAVE ME
ALONE.

And
that
was
where
things
seemed
to
settle.

47

Then the new Olympics were announced. RUSSIA was to have its greatest team **ever**.

It had someone who could hit a baseball farther than anybody.

It had someone who could kick a football farther than anybody.

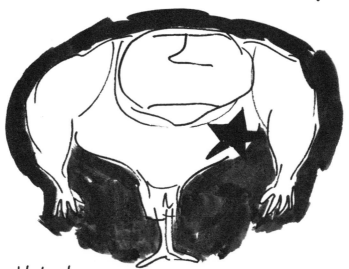

It had someone who could run a mile faster than anybody.

The State Department called a conference.

So they sent a representative—

who returned with a message.

So they checked his loyalty file.

And that seemed to be the answer. Harold Swerg
was just not interested in belonging. A higher
State Department official went to see him.

BUT YOU'VE **GOT**
TO **BELONG!**
EVERYONE
BELONGS TO
SOMETHING!

NOT ME. said
Harold
Swerg.

They sent a bunch of congressmen.

IT'S THE RULE OF A DEMOCRACY THAT THE MAJORITY
DECIDES. A MAJORITY HAS DECIDED THEY WANT **YOU**
TO PLAY IN THE OLYMPICS. ARE YOU TRYING TO
CRUMBLE OUR FOUNDATIONS?

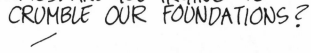

"I'M JUST TRYING TO BE
LEFT ALONE" said
Harold Swerg and
he sent them away.

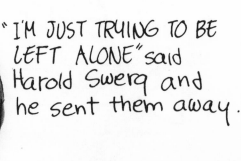

screamed the press. Congress threatened to draft
him into the Olympics.

Finally there came a special
appeal from the President.

DO
YOU
WANT
US
TO
LOSE?

SO **THATS**
WHATS
BOTHERING
EVERYBODY.

BUT WHAT'S
WRONG WITH
LOSING ?
IT'S ONLY
A GAME.

Everyone was thrown into confusion.

LOSING IS JUST
THE OTHER SIDE
OF WINNING.
SOMEBODY
HAS TO DO IT.

"DON'T LISTEN! DON'T LISTEN!" cried the President's advisors and they all closed their ears.

The public expressed its outrage. They booed. They
hissed. They burned Olympic torches on his lawn.

The Soviet press offered its views on
the subject.

Then one day, just when things were at their hottest - Harold Swerg came out of his house and said:

ALLRIGHT.
I'LL PLAY.

"**SWERG WILL PLAY!**" The country was electrified.
"**SWERG WILL PLAY!**" Both political parties claimed credit. And so the games began!

The first event was who could hit a baseball the farthest. The Russian (Peoples Farthest Baseball Hero Smedyakov) went first.

912 FEET 6 INCHES!

Harold Swerq went second.

912 FEET 6 INCHES!

The next event was who could kick a football the farthest. The Russian (People's Hero Kicker Bros-nokopski) went first.

PUNT

310
YARDS
4 FEET
1 INCH!

Harold Swerg went second.

PUNT

310
YARDS
4 FEET
1 INCH!

Grumblings of discontent began to murmur through the crowd.

The last event was the mile. His opponent was Peoples Fastest Hero Runner Alive Kchawelshkov.

It was a tie.

Harold Swerg was called before the judges.

HAROLD SWERG, YOU WERE
NOT GIVING YOUR ALL!

I
CERTAINLY
WAS" said Harold
Swerg
indig-
nantly.

" THEN WHY DIDN'T YOU WIN demanded the judges.

"WINNING DOESN'T
TAKE MY ALL" said
Harold
Swerg
"EQUALLING
TAKES
MY
ALL."

"HUH?" said the judges

LETS
SEE
YOU
TRY
TO
KICK —
A
FOOTBALL
EXACTLY
310
YARDS
4 FEET
1 INCH

But the judges just didn't understand.

IT WAS
QUITE A
CHALLENGE.
I
WASN'T
SURE I
COULD
DO
IT.

ANYBODY WHO WANTS
ANY RECORDS EQUALLED
COME ON AROUND!

But nobody did.

Because nobody is interested
in having records equalled.

So they left Harold Swerg alone.—

which was just the way he wanted it.

SUPERMAN

A WOMAN *starts across the stage.* MUGGER *runs from behind her, stops in front of her and poses threateningly.*

MUGGER   Don't scream. Give me your purse!

WOMAN   I wasn't going to scream. I was going to try to discuss this with you.

MUGGER   It won't work. Three times this week broads discussed me out of taking their pocketbooks. I got to live *too*, you know.

SUPERMAN (*Off stage*)   Faster than the speed of light!

MUGGER   Oh, my God!

SUPERMAN (*Off stage*)   More powerful than an express train!

MUGGER   It's—it's—

SUPERMAN (*Off stage*)   Leaps over buildings in a single bound!

MUGGER (*Flees*)   Superman!

SUPERMAN (*Enters running and leaping*)   Ha! Ha! That scoundrel won't harm you again, madam. Else he'll have to reckon with *Superman!*

WOMAN (*Stares disbelieving*)   What is this? A gag?

SUPERMAN   Indeed no, madam. Superman does not gag. (*Proudly*) Superman doesn't have a sense of humor!

WOMAN   You can't really be—

SUPERMAN   Ha, ha! But I am!

WOMAN   You mean—who I used to hear all the time on the radio?

SUPERMAN   Superman, madam! Superman!

WOMAN (*Suspiciously*)   Who sponsored you?

SUPERMAN (*Proudly*)   Corn Kix, madam!

WOMAN (*Suspiciously*)   Who were you on just before?

SUPERMAN   Mandrake the Magician, madam. But you wouldn't remember him.

WOMAN   Oh, wouldn't I? With Lothar?

SUPERMAN   By George!

WOMAN (*Still suspicious*)   And who was on *after* you?

SUPERMAN   Jack Armstrong, all-American boy!

WOMAN (*Sings*)   Raise the flag for Hudson High, boys—

SUPERMAN (*Sings*)   Won't you try Wheaties, the best breakfast food in the land. (*Stops himself*) That wasn't true, you know. Corn Kix was better.

WOMAN   Do you remember "I Love A Mystery"?

SUPERMAN (*Excited*)   With, Jack, Doc and Reggie?

WOMAN (*Hums the theme.* SUPERMAN *joins her. The* WOMAN *stops as* SUPERMAN *continues to hum. She stares hard at him*)   There's something wrong.

SUPERMAN (*Politely*)   Madam?

WOMAN   Doesn't that costume make you look lumpy when you wear your street clothes? I mean, the cape and all?

SUPERMAN   Well, it *is* a little warm. I usually take off summers.

WOMAN   Why do you wear it?

SUPERMAN   What?

WOMAN   *You* know what I mean. The costume. The cape.

SUPERMAN   It's the uniform of Superman, madam.

WOMAN   It's rather effeminate don't you think?

SUPERMAN   Hold on!

WOMAN   It *is* terribly skin-tight. You're not a transvestite, are you? You don't have to answer if you don't want to.

SUPERMAN   A *what?*

WOMAN (*Leering suspiciously*)   *You* know. Do you rescue more men than women?

SUPERMAN   I rescue only those in dire straits!

WOMAN   Why?

SUPERMAN (*Shaken*)   What? Why what? What?

WOMAN   Why this compulsion to rescue. Are you a cop? Do you get paid for it? Is it your job?

SUPERMAN   Well, nobody *hired* me, if that's what you mean.

WOMAN   Then, you just do it for kicks. Run around in your skin-tight blue leotards and rescue people for the thrill of it.

SUPERMAN (*Weakly*)   I fight crime.

WOMAN   You can't fight crime in a business suit?

SUPERMAN (*Sadly*)   You think I'm an exhibitionist.

WOMAN   You *could* spend more time reading.

SUPERMAN   I think it's wrong to judge Superman the way you judge *other* people.

WOMAN   Everybody thinks he's special. But they don't run around in skin-tight, effeminate leotards—

SUPERMAN (*Hotly*) All right, so I do rescue more men than women—but more men get into trouble than women! *I'm* all right.

WOMAN I didn't say a word.

SUPERMAN Well, I know what you're thinking.

WOMAN How come you're not married?

SUPERMAN (*Weakly*) I fight crime—most of the time.

WOMAN (*Shrugs*) A man your age.

SUPERMAN You can't judge me the way you judge earth people. I admit that if I came from earth and wore effeminate skin-tight leotards and rescued more men than women it *would* seem suspicious—but I'm from *Krypton!*

WOMAN Look, I'm not arguing.

SUPERMAN Well, I don't want you to go away with the wrong idea.

WOMAN If it makes you more secure to be what you call Superman—

SUPERMAN I *am*, I tell you, I *am*. Do you want me to prove it? Do you want me to leap over a tall building in a single bound?

WOMAN Honey, you don't have to prove anything to me. Why *hurt* yourself? What are these doubts that torment you so terribly that you have to go around proving your masculinity to everybody?

SUPERMAN (*Bitterly*) O.K. Have it your way. I'm not Superman, all right? You feel better? I'm not! It's all a gag! All right?

WOMAN You'll see. You've come to a wise conclusion.

SUPERMAN But you *will* admit I'm better than average?

WOMAN (*Warmly*) I'm *sure* you are.

SUPERMAN (*Gratefully*) Can I take you to the theatre tomorrow night?

WOMAN I'm washing my hair.

SUPERMAN The next night?

WOMAN I'm sorry, I'm busy.

SUPERMAN Well, can I see you sometime?

WOMAN Well, the evenings are hard. Maybe for lunch. You won't wear that—that costume.

SUPERMAN No—a suit. I swear—a suit. I'll go out this minute and buy a suit.

WOMAN What's the matter? You're standing funny.

SUPERMAN I've got a stomach ache.

WOMAN Do you need help? Can you get home all right?

SUPERMAN It's only a little way. I think I can make it if I go slow. You're very considerate.

WOMAN Take it easy. And don't rush around so much. You'll find that you'll feel better.

SUPERMAN (*Begins to exit bent over*) You've been a great help. I'll be in touch.

WOMAN (*Calls to him*) Drink some hot soup! (*She turns to exit. The* MUGGER *leaps out at her*)

MUGGER Don't scream. Give me your purse!

WOMAN (*Screams*) Superman! Come quick! Superman!

SUPERMAN (*Completely bent over, clutching his stomach, turns weakly toward her*) Who?

The Lonely Machine

Other people always disappointed Walter Fay—

TRAITORS.

Other people were always either ignoring him—

I'M A PERSON!

Or rejecting him —

I'M A PERSON!

Or betraying him —

I'M **NOT** A PERSON?

This made Walter Fay sulk a lot:

OTHER PEOPLE ALWAYS DO WHAT **THEY** WANT TO DO - **NEVER** WHAT **I** WANT THEM TO DO.

OTHER PEOPLE DON'T SEE ME THE WAY **I** SEE ME :-

- A **SWEETHEART** OF A GUY - MAYBE A LITTLE QUIET AT FIRST BUT IF YOU ENCOURAGE HIM - **LOTS** OF LAUGHS - FUNNY STORIES -

DEEP OBSER- VATIONS.

BY MYSELF I GET ALONG FINE—BUT PUT ME IN A ROOM WITH ONE OTHER PERSON— I BECOME ONLY HALF OF ME.

PUT ME IN A ROOM WITH TWO OTHER PEOPLE — I'M A TENTH OF ME.
PUT ME IN A ROOM WITH A MOB AND I'M **NOBODY!**

THE MORE PEOPLE I'M WITH THE LESS OF ME IT IS WHO'S THERE.

THE MORE I'M ALONE THE MORE OF ME THERE IS TO BE ALONE WITH.

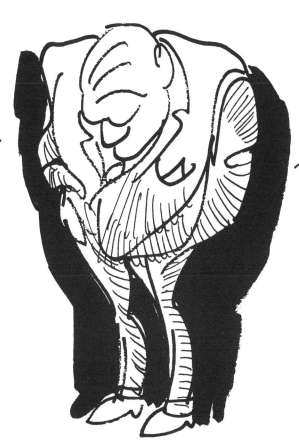

And so he'd regularly vow never to go out again.

Walter Fay was the kind of man who hated parties.

He always said: THERE'S NO SUCH THING AS REAL CONVERSATION AT A PARTY.

He always said:

I'VE NEVER MET A GIRL I LIKED AT A PARTY.

He always said:

I REALLY DON'T KNOW WHY I GO.

Walter Fay regularly fell in love at every party he went to . . . .

THERE'S NO SUCH THING AS REAL
CONVERSATION AT A PARTY. I'VE
NEVER MET A MAN I LIKED AT
A PARTY. I REALLY DON'T
KNOW WHY I GO.

I
LOVE
YOU.

Eventually his love
always disappointed
him —

I'M
BUSY
TOMORROW.

Ignored him —

I'M BUSY THE
DAY AFTER
TOMORROW.

rejected him —

I'M BUSY THE DAY
AFTER THE DAY
AFTER TOMORROW.

and betrayed him —

ANYWAY,
YOU'RE TOO
SHORT.

But it wasn't just the girls he loved who disappointed, ignored, rejected and betrayed him— HELLO, MOTHER, THIS IS WALTER—

WALTER, HOW COME YOU ALWAYS CALL DURING "BEN CASEY"?

The world had no time for Walter Fay. He tried to be alone but it was too hard—

IF ONLY NOT BEING ALONE DIDN'T DEPEND ON OTHER PEOPLE.

Nobody ever called him. He always had to call other people.

OTHER
PEOPLE
MUST
HAVE
VERY
SMALL
PHONE
BILLS.

He knew what one of his problems was—

So one day Walter Fay made a decision. If other people didn't need him he wouldn't need other people!

OTHER PEOPLE
ARE MY
ENEMY!

And that's how he saw his life up till now— A battle between himself and his **enemies!**

When it was between himself and a girl he had called it "**the battle of the sexes**."

When it was between himself and a boss he had called it "**class warfare**."

When it was between himself and his family he had called it "**neurosis**."

Walter Fay well knew that one did not go to his enemies for assistance – one went to his friends –

So one day Walter Fay went down to his basement –

and invented himself a Lonely Machine.

IT'S MINE! IT'S ALL MINE!

I NEVER HAD ANYTHING THAT WAS ALL MINE BEFORE.

The Lonely Machine did whatever he wanted it to do. It listened to him.

It took long walks in the country with him. It looked at the stars with him.

Walter Fay invented it a voice so it could say nice things—

There was not a need Walter Fay had that the machine did not answer. It was a mother to him—

It was a father to him—

It was his lover—

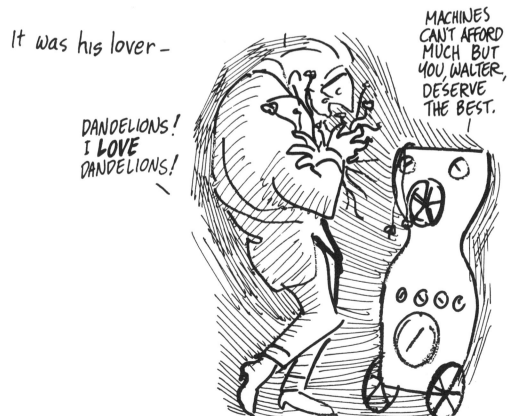

For the first time Walter Fay could be himself with another — he could let loose —
he could be aggressive!

He could feel self-pity.

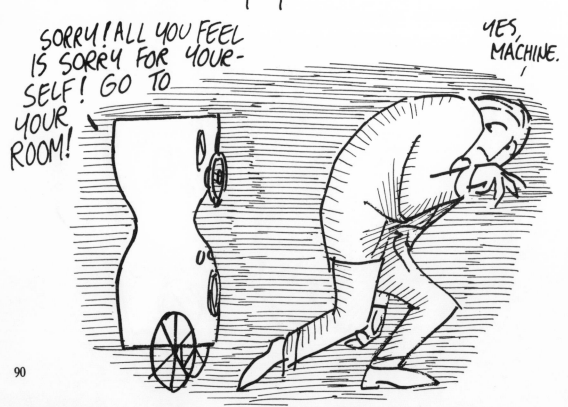

He could be forgiving.

Walter Fay had a relationship.

He swelled with a new assurance-

But being perfect where he had always been perfect was not enough for Walter Fay.

He wanted to be perfect on **enemy** ground.

He started going to parties again.

Now that he didn't need anybody, didn't care for anybody, he began being invited everywhere.

SORRY, OLD MACHINE— DINNER OUT AGAIN TONIGHT. — THE KENNEDYS.

HAVE A NICE TIME, WALTER. DON'T WORRY — ABOUT ME.

He knew the machine was hurt. But he also knew something else - that he enjoyed hurting the machine. He was philosophical about it.

THAT'S LIFE. TAXI !

He played the machine against his new friends and his new friends against the machine.

CAN'T SEE YOU TOMORROW NIGHT, KIDS. DUTY CALLS AT HOME, Y'KNOW.

HAVE A NICE TIME, WALTER. DON'T WORRY ABOUT US.

But home wasn't as much fun as it used to be—

YOU'RE BORED WITH ME.

DON'T BE FOOLISH.

Walter Fay started coming home later. He always hoped the machine would be asleep. It never was.

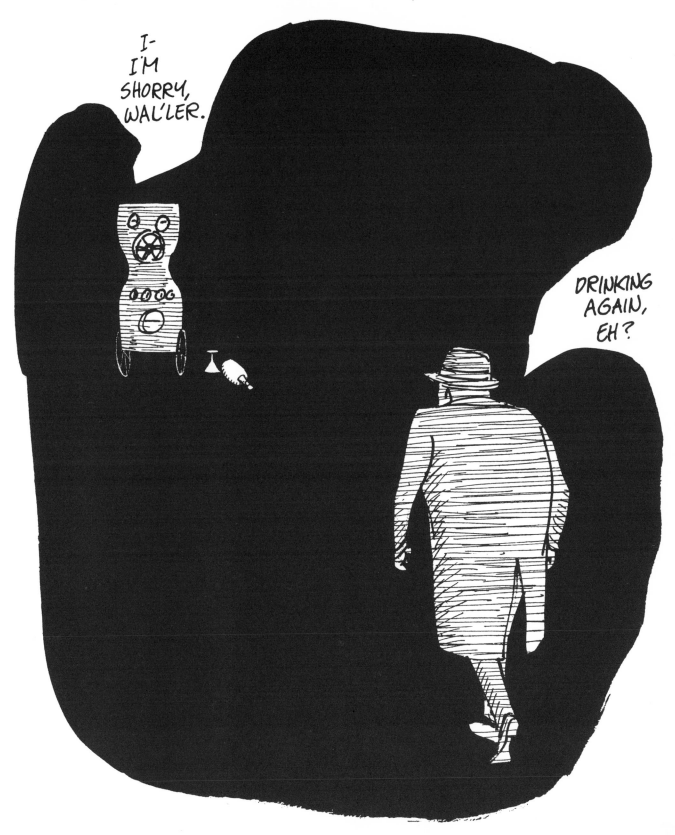

I- I'M SHORRY, WAL'LER.

DRINKING AGAIN, EH?

The point was that Walter Fay needed something when he needed it and not after he stopped needing it.

THE MACHINE WAS ONLY A MEANS TO AN END,
Walter Fay explained to himself.

IT WAS A BRIDGE BETWEEN ME AND OTHER PEOPLE.
He saw it all clearly now.

LONELY MACHINES ARE SPLENDID BUT THEY HAVE THEIR PLACE.

Walter Fay had outgrown his machine.

IT'S NOBODY'S FAULT.

One day he made an announcement..

MACHINE, OLD FRIEND, IT'S NOT GOING TO BE EASY TO TELL YOU THIS.

BREAK MY HEART. I'VE BEEN EXPECTING IT.

I'M BRINGING A YOUNG LADY TO LIVE HERE NEXT WEEK.

BREAK MY HEART. I'VE BEEN EXPECTING IT.

So a stranger named Mercedes came to live in the home of Walter Fay and the machine.

She was a mother to him—

She was a father to him—

She was his lover—

But at odd moments when Mercedes was out organiz-
ing a charity drive Walter Fay would wheel out his
lonely machine.

But there no longer seemed to be any contact

and receiving no answer, he wheeled it into the upstairs closet and never wheeled it out again.

And there it remained until one day Mercedes came upon it—

WALTER— WHAT A LOVELY SURPRISE! — A DRESS- MAKER'S DUMMY!

And she made many dresses and gave many parties and Walter Fay never felt disappointed, ignored, rejected or betrayed — or any other feeling again.

Not even for a second

Crawling Arnold

The curtain rises on a projection: an enormous color slide of a smiling baby. The stage is dark and voices come out of the darkness. Everybody "oohs" and "ahhhs" at the projection.

BARRY   That's little Will at six months.

GRACE   Eight months, dear. Even little Will wasn't that big at six months.

BARRY   Seven months then. What a big bad bandit of a boy, eh, Miss Sympathy?

MISS SYMPATHY   An alert child.

BARRY *(Clicks slide changer)*   Next slide please. *(The projection changes)*   There he is at only one year! Did you ever see such a rough and tough customer, Miss Sympathy?

GRACE   Fourteen months, dear.

BARRY   Thirteen months.

MISS SYMPATHY   He does seem like an alert child.

BARRY   Alert? You should see him crawl around down in the shelter. Arnold just goes down when the siren sounds and sits there. But little Will! He has to touch everything. Won't keep out of anything—the oxygen tank, the gas masks, the plastic bombs—

MISS SYMPATHY   The shelter? *(The lights come up slowly to reveal the expensively bedecked patio of the* ENTERPRISE *home.* BARRY *and* GRACE ENTERPRISE, *a vigorous, athletic couple in their seventies are sitting with* MISS SYMPATHY, *a young and pretty social worker, in deck chairs partly facing the slide screen. The projector is behind them being operated by* MILLIE, *the Negro maid. She, expressionlessly, begins to wheel it off)*

BARRY   Our *fallout* shelter! Wait till you see it! *(To* MILLIE*)* You can serve our helmets now, Millie.
*(*MILLIE *coolly exits.* BARRY *and* GRACE *look hostilely after her)*

GRACE   It's the only shelter in the country that has a television set and a whatayoucall them dear?

BARRY   Stereo rig.

GRACE   Stereo rig.
(She begins to fuss with the baby, making small gurgling noises at it)

MISS SYMPATHY   A television set? But what good would a—

BARRY   It's not a real television set. It's the frame of one and then I have a sixteen millimeter movie projector and a library of films—*Tim McCoy, Our Gang*—a variety of fare. The idea, you understand, is that under enemy attack the family can survive down there for *weeks*, while being able to simulate normal conditions of living. For example, I've had cards made up with the names of our favorite shows and at the time they would ordinarily go on, we run a picture—a slide picture on the screen showing the title of the show—

GRACE   *Lassie—Ben Casey—*

BARRY   And during the half-hours those shows normally run, we sit and reminisce about our favorite episodes.

MISS SYMPATHY   You've *done* this?

BARRY   Several times. Before Little Will was born, Mrs. Enterprise and I—*and Arnold*—used to spend many happy weeks—many happy weeks in our shelter.

GRACE   One gets to *know* Ben Casey so much more deeply after one has talked about him in a fallout shelter for two weeks. *(*MILLIE *enters with four air-raid helmets on a serving tray. There is evident tension between herself and the* ENTERPRISES. BARRY *and* GRACE *each sullenly take a helmet)* You may serve cocktails now, Millie.
*(*GRACE *places a helmet in baby carriage.* MISS SYMPATHY *quietly demurs)*

BARRY   You're making a mistake, Miss Sympathy. Today's drill begins pretty soon.
*(*MILLIE *exits with* MISS SYMPATHY *looking after her, curiously)*
You should see our library down there! Four years' worth of back copies of the *Readers Digest.* I didn't know how long we'd be down there so I wanted to get articles of *lasting* interest.
(He takes the baby carriage from GRACE *and begins to fuss with the baby, making small gurgling noises)*

GRACE *(Proudly)*   It's the only shelter in the country to be written up in *Good Housekeeping*.

MISS SYMPATHY   Little Will is how old?

GRACE *(Proudly)*   He'll be—

BARRY *(Jealously)*   He'll be two in September. *(He buries his face in the blankets of the carriage, muffling the sound of his voice)* Isn't this the biggest, baddest, toughest little fellow who ever lived? I'll tell the world this is the biggest, baddest, toughest little fellow who ever lived!

MISS SYMPATHY *(Peering into the carriage)*   My, he's a *large* baby.

BARRY   Arnold was half his size at that age. Arnold couldn't crawl until he was almost *two.* Little Will's been crawling for four months now. *Four* months.

MISS SYMPATHY   And Arnold?

BARRY *(Nervously)*   Wasn't Millie supposed to bring us some drinks?

GRACE   Well, that's why we asked you to come, Miss Sympathy.

BARRY *(Embarrassed)*   Yes. Arnold is crawling again too. For four months.

GRACE (*Sadly*)   Regressed.

MISS SYMPATHY (*Taking out a pad and making notes*)   That sometimes happens when the first child feels over-competitive with the second child. *Sibling rivalry.*

GRACE   Crawl. As soon as he enters the house he falls on all fours and crawls, crawls, crawls. I say to him, "Arnold, you *know* you can walk beautifully. At business you walk beautifully—"

MISS SYMPATHY   At business?

BARRY (*Embarrassed*)   Arnold is thirty-five.
(*He fusses with the carriage*)

MISS SYMPATHY (*Making a long note*)   *Advanced* sibling rivalry.

GRACE (*Distressed*)   That's what we wanted to talk to you about. I know there's nothing seriously wrong with Arnold. He's always been a good boy. Done everything we told him. Never talked back. Always well-mannered. Never been a show-off.

MISS SYMPATHY (*Taking notes*)   He's never had any previously crawling history?

GRACE   I'm afraid he took the news of Little Will's birth rather hard. I imagine when one has been raised as an only child and has lived happily all one's years in one's parents' home, it's hard to welcome a little stranger.

BARRY (*Buries his head in the blankets, muffling his voice*)   Who's Daddy's brave big bandit of a man? Little Will's Daddy's brave big bandit of a man.

GRACE   Please, dear. Don't talk with your mouth full. (MILLIE *enters with three drinks on a platter. A coolness immediately settles in the room.* BARRY *and* GRACE *lapse into a sullen silence.* GRACE *coldly receives her drink*) Thank you, Millie.
(BARRY *grumbles something under his breath as he receives his.* MISS SYMPATHY *is obviously perturbed*)

MISS SYMPATHY (*Whispers to* MILLIE *as she is served her drink*)   I strongly sympathize with the aspirations of your people.
(MILLIE *exits*)

BARRY (*Rocking the carriage*)   A nationwide alert! All the American people mobilized as one, sitting it out in shelters all over the country. That's what I'd like Little Will to grow up to see. I guess it's just an old man's dream.

GRACE   Here's Arnold! Please, Miss Sympathy, don't tell him you're here because we asked—

ARNOLD   (*Enters crawling. He is an attractive young man in his thirties. He wears a hat and a business suit and carries an attaché case*) Father—Mother—(*He notices* MISS SYMPATHY, *sizes her up for a long moment then coolly turns to his mother*) Company?

GRACE   Arnold, dear, this is Miss Sympathy. Miss Sympathy, this is our son, Arnold Enterprise.

MISS SYMPATHY   I'm pleased to meet you.

ARNOLD (*Turning away*)   That's O.K. (*To his mother*) Dinner ready?

BARRY   You're being damned rude, Arnold!

ARNOLD   I apologize. I have things on my mind. Are you having drinks?

GRACE   Oh, I'm sorry dear. With you on the floor that way I forget that you drink.

ARNOLD   Occasionally to excess. (*Crawls around*) Did anyone see my coloring book?

GRACE   Millie!
(ARNOLD *crawls around. There is an awkward pause.* MILLIE, *finally, enters with a drink.* MISS SYMPATHY *leans forward examining everyone's reaction*)

ARNOLD *(Accepting the drink)* It's got an olive in it!

GRACE Please, dear.

ARNOLD *(To MILLIE)* You know I drink martinis with a lemon peel!

GRACE *(Placating)* Millie—would you mind—
(MILLIE *coolly takes back the glass and starts off*)

MISS SYMPATHY *(Whispers to MILLIE as she exits)* I have great regard for the aspirations of your people!

GRACE *(To ARNOLD)* Did you have to—

ARNOLD *(To himself)* When I began drinking martinis ten years ago I ordered them with an olive. I didn't know any better, I guess. They always came back with a lemon peel. *(To MISS SYMPATHY)* There was something so garbagey about a lemon peel lying at the bottom of my martini.

BARRY *(Angry)* Arnold! I'm sorry, Miss Sympathy.

MISS SYMPATHY *(Waving BARRY off)* No. No. I understand. *(To ARNOLD)* Please go on.

ARNOLD *(Shrugs)* There's nothing to go on. I got used to it. I got to like it. I got to *want* lemon peels in my martinis. It still looked garbagey, but I found that *exciting!* I've always been surrounded by lots of money, cut off from life. That lemon peel floating there in its oil slick that way was to me my only contact with The People. It reminded me of East *River* movies—the Dead End Kids. Remember the Dead End Kids?

MISS SYMPATHY No, I'm afraid not—

ARNOLD *(Suspiciously)* What do you *do*?
(BARRY *and* GRACE *look distressed.* MISS SYMPATHY *warns them off with her eyes*)

MISS SYMPATHY I'm a social worker.

ARNOLD *(Astonished)* And you don't remember the Dead End Kids?

MISS SYMPATHY A *psychiatric* social worker.

ARNOLD Oh, *you'd* remember Ingrid Bergman movies. Where's my coloring book, Mother?

GRACE Where did you leave it yesterday, dear?

ARNOLD *(Restlessly)* I've got to find my coloring book. I feel in the mood for coloring.

GRACE I'll help you look, Arnold, if you'll just tell me where you think you left it.
(ARNOLD, *perturbed, crawls around the room looking for his coloring book.* GRACE *follows him anxiously.* BARRY, *flushed with embarrassment, rocks the baby carriage almost violently*)

BARRY That's a good boy, Little Will, that's a nice, big good boy Little Will.

ARNOLD I found it!
(He crawls off in a corner with the coloring book. GRACE follows him. As he begins coloring, she looks over his shoulder)

BARRY *(Miserably, to MISS SYMPATHY)* I've tried to know that boy.

MISS SYMPATHY Communications between the generations is never easy, Mr. Enterprise.

BARRY We wrote away to Dear Abby about him. She was snotty.

MISS SYMPATHY I'm not sure you acted wisely. She's not licensed, you know.

BARRY I tried in every way to get close to him, like a father should.

MISS SYMPATHY Perhaps if you had been a bit more patient—

BARRY   I've tried, believe me, I've tried. I introduced him into my way of life—my friends—
I even got him accepted into my athletic club, and they don't usually take Jews.

MISS SYMPATHY   Arnold's Jewish?

BARRY   *That* week. It's not worth discussing. The next week he converted to Buddhism. They
don't take Buddhists at my club either. But I got him in. It didn't do any good. All he ever did
was go down to the gym and ride one of those vibrating horses for hours. He'd just sit there
and ride till closing time. And he'd have a far-away look in his eyes. It became the scandal
of the club.

GRACE *(To* ARNOLD*)*   The sky is blue, dear. Not red; *blue*.

ARNOLD   Picasso colors it red.

GRACE   Picasso is an artist, dear. Artists can color the sky red because they *know* it's blue.
Those of us who aren't artists must color things the way they really are or people might
think we're stupid.

BARRY *(Flushed, strides over to* ARNOLD*)*   For Christ's sake, stop embarrassing us in front of
the woman! Color the goddamn sky blue!
(He glares over ARNOLD's *shoulder.* GRACE *flutters nervously over to* MISS SYMPATHY*)*

GRACE   Another drink perhaps, Miss Sympathy?

MISS SYMPATHY   I'm fine, thank you. You mustn't allow yourself to get too depressed, Mrs.
Enterprise.

GRACE *(Hopefully)*   I manage to keep myself busy. Organizational work. I'm the block captain
of the "Let's Be A Friend to our Children Society." It's made up of mothers who've had somber
histories with their children and are trying to profit others with their experience.

MISS SYMPATHY   That sounds very ambitious.

GRACE   And I'm chairman of the gratification committee of the Husband's Fulfillment League.
We prepare and distribute many useful pamphlets based on lessons learned from many somber experiences with fulfillment. And, of course, there's still tennis.

MISS SYMPATHY   It all sounds very ambitious.

GRACE   But primarily my life has been my husband's. When he's happy I try to be happy.
When he's unhappy I try to be unhappy. When he wants me I try to want him. The key to a
successful marriage is giving. *I've* given. Everything.
*(*MILLIE *enters and serves* ARNOLD *his drink)*

ARNOLD   That's it. A lemon peel! *(He drops coloring book and examines the martini)*
I can't tolerate a martini without a lemon peel. *(To* MILLIE*)* Have you been back to the U.N.,
Millie?

MILLIE *(Coolly)*   Not since last time.

ARNOLD *(To* MISS SYMPATHY*)*   Millie was on television at the U.N. We all watched her.

MISS SYMPATHY *(Interested)*   Oh, what were you doing there?
*(*GRACE *and* BARRY *writhe uncomfortably)*

MILLIE   Rioting.
(She exits)

BARRY *(Furious)*   I swear we've got to replace that girl.

GRACE   It doesn't do any good. Any of the girls you get these days, they're all the same. One
time or another they've *all* rioted at the U.N.

MISS SYMPATHY   I, naturally, don't agree with her means but if we examine her motivation we should be able to understand why she may have felt that such a form of protest was in order. A misguided protest, I admit, but—

BARRY   She wants her own shelter!

MISS SYMPATHY   What?

BARRY   When I started work on the shelter I was going to build two of them. One for us and one for Millie and any friends she'd want to invite. Same dimensions, same material, exactly like ours in every way.

GRACE   Millie resented the idea.

BARRY   That girl has been with us ten years, hardly a peep out of her in all that time. Before her, the girl we used to take in was Millie's mother. When Millie's mother was ill, her *grand-mother* would come in to clean.

GRACE   Millie's grandmother was a *good* girl.

BARRY   We never had any trouble before. But when I tell Millie I'm building her a shelter, same dimensions, same material, exactly like ours in every way—she nearly quits!

MISS SYMPATHY   I sympathize with her aspirations. She wanted to share *your* shelter of course.

BARRY *(Outraged)*   Yes!

MISS SYMPATHY   You see, while on the surface it would seem that the two shelters are alike in every way, the simple fact that Millie is excluded from one of them can have a devastating psychological effort on her. I have always been opposed to separate but equal fallout shelters.

BARRY   But now she *wants* one!

MISS SYMPATHY   Oh?

BARRY   She comes back from the U.N. and we're having a practice air-raid drill—and you understand we're all Americans here, *we* accept the law of the land—so we invite Millie into our shelter. And she refuses! Suddenly she wants her *own* shelter!

MISS SYMPATHY   But why? For what reason?

GRACE *(Distraught)*   She says she's a neutralist!

ARNOLD   She's a hypocrite. A real neutralist wouldn't take shelter at all.

BARRY   Do you hear that kid? He's worse than she is!

MISS SYMPATHY   Are you a neutralist, Arnold?

ARNOLD   No, the neutralists are too extreme. I'm neutral.

GRACE *(Maneuvering to leave* MISS SYMPATHY *alone with* ARNOLD*)*   Barry dear, don't you think we should make a final check of the shelter. The drill should start any time now.

BARRY   Good thinking. I wonder what the delay is? The block captain mentioned last week that they were having a little trouble with the siren.
(They exit wheeling the baby carriage)

MISS SYMPATHY *(There is an awkward silence. She decides to get right to it)*   Don't you know how to walk?

ARNOLD   That's a funny question. Why do you ask?

MISS SYMPATHY   Well, you're not walking.

ARNOLD   I'm not smoking either. Why don't you ask me if I know how to smoke?

MISS SYMPATHY *(Containing herself)*   That's very good. *(ARNOLD shrugs)* Do you mind if I crawl with you?

ARNOLD *(Hotly)*   Yes, I do!

MISS SYMPATHY   But *you* do it!

ARNOLD   I do it because I believe in it. You do it because you think you're being therapeutic. You're not. You're only being patronizing. I realize that in your field it's sometimes difficult to tell the difference.

MISS SYMPATHY *(With difficulty)*   That's very good.

ARNOLD   If you really feel the urge to crawl with me—*really* feel it, I mean—then you'll be most welcome. Not any more welcome or unwelcome than you are now by the way. I am by no means a missionary. Did you see my coloring book?

MISS SYMPATHY   When anyone says anything you don't like you retreat into that coloring book.

ARNOLD   I admit it's rude. I shouldn't do it unless I have a coloring book for you too. *(He studies her)* Do you wear glasses?

MISS SYMPATHY   Contact lenses.

ARNOLD *(Suddenly shy)*   You'd be prettier with glasses. Or rather *I* think you'd be prettier with glasses. I like the way a girl looks with glasses. It makes her face look—less undressed.

MISS SYMPATHY   You think contact lenses make me look naked?

ARNOLD   I think the more people have on the better they get along with each other. If everybody in the world wore big hats, thick glasses and dark overcoats they'd all pass each other by thinking, "What an interesting person must be inside all that." And they'd be curious, but they wouldn't ask questions. Who'd dare ask questions like "What are you really like" to a person in a big hat, thick glasses and a dark overcoat? The desire to invade privacy rises in direct proportion to the amount of clothing a person takes off. It's what we call "communication." Take off the big hat and they say, "Good morning, sir!" Take off the thick glasses and they say, "My, don't you have *haunted* eyes!" Take off the overcoat and they say, "Tell me *everything!*" So there you have intimacy, followed by understanding, followed by disillusion, followed by—*(Shrugs)* if only everybody wore more clothing we wouldn't have wars.

MISS SYMPATHY   You're saying you'd like to wear an overcoat with me. Is that it?

ARNOLD   I'd feel better if one of us at least wore a big hat. Do you ever have fantasies?

MISS SYMPATHY   Aren't you getting intimate?

ARNOLD   *You* decided to wear the contact lenses.

MISS SYMPATHY   Everybody has fantasies.

ARNOLD   What are yours about?

MISS SYMPATHY   Being a better social worker.

ARNOLD   Dear God.

MISS SYMPATHY *(Sadly)*   I used to have fantasies about Adlai Stevenson. But that's all over now.

ARNOLD   I have fantasies all the time. When I'm awake, when I'm asleep, I *live* with them. I embellish them. Polish them day after day. You cultivate a good fantasy long enough and soon it can seep out into the real world. Do you know how old my parents are?

MISS SYMPATHY   I hadn't thought of it. Middle fifties?

ARNOLD   They're both over seventy.

MISS SYMPATHY   And they had a *baby*?

ARNOLD *(Shrugs, reaches for the coloring book, changes his mind)*   My father doesn't look very much older than me does he?

MISS SYMPATHY *(Evasive)*   I don't know if I noticed.

ARNOLD   You're kind. But that's how it's been always. They're both alert, involved, aggressive people. So while I'm out trying, unsuccessfully, to make it with a girl and I come home, mixed up and angry and feeling like not much of anything, what are they waiting up proudly to tell me? *They're* having a baby. I'll try to say this in as uninvolved and unneurotic a way as I know how—it's hard to face a daily series of piddling, eroding defeats and, in addition, have the fact thrown in your face that your *father* at *age seventy* can still do better than you can. *(There is a long pause.* ARNOLD *fishes a ball out from under a chair and tosses it to* MISS SYMPATHY. *She one-hands it)* You catch pretty good. *(She cocks her arm back.* ARNOLD *throws out one hand defensively)* No, don't throw it. I'm not ready to compete yet.

MISS SYMPATHY   These fantasies—were any of them about crawling?

ARNOLD   In my fantasies, it was everyone else who crawled. For instance, in one of them I had this uncle. Uncle Walter—
(A weak siren begins to wail erratically)

BARRY *(Enters, running with the baby carriage)*   That's it! The alert! Down to the shelter everyone!

GRACE *(Enters with a fire extinguisher and shopping bag)*   Oh, it's so exciting! It's so exciting!
*(*BARRY *switches on a transistor radio)*

RADIO VOICE   Stay tuned to this frequency. All other frequencies have left the air. This is Conelrad!

BARRY *(Listening intently)*   I met that fellow down at civil-defense headquarters once. You'd be surprised. He's just like you and me.
*(*GRACE *is in a sudden, heated conversation with* ARNOLD*)*

GRACE   But you *have* to go down! You went down with us last year!

RADIO VOICE   It is the law that everyone on the street take shelter—

ARNOLD   We're *not* on the street. We're on the patio.

BARRY *(Exasperated)*   You think the Russians give a damn we're not on the street?

GRACE   It's the spirit of the law one should follow, dear.

BARRY   Arnold, I've had enough of this nonsense! Downstairs! That's a parental order!

ARNOLD *(Hotly)*   I colored the sky blue, didn't I? Why don't *you* ever meet *me* halfway?

BARRY *(Exits wheeling the baby carriage)*   I can't do anything with him.

GRACE   We can't leave our oldest out on the patio!

BARRY *(Re-enters with the baby carriage)*   He's the one who's breaking the law. Let's go!
(He exits with the carriage)

GRACE   You'd better follow me, Miss Sympathy. It's dark in the basement.

MISS SYMPATHY *(Weakly, to* ARNOLD*)*   It *is* the law.

ARNOLD   I told you I'm not asking for converts.

GRACE   For the last time, won't you come, Arnold? It's not going to be any fun without you.

ARNOLD   I'm doing something *else*, Mother.

BARRY *(Re-enters with the baby carriage)*   The hell with him. The law doesn't mean a thing to *our* son. Come on!
(He exits with the baby carriage. GRACE *exits)*

MISS SYMPATHY *(To* ARNOLD*)*   I, as do you, question the sense of such a drill, but objecting to this law by defying it robs *all* laws of their meaning. Now, I can see working for its reform while continuing to *obey* it, but to be both against it and defy it at the same time seems to me to weaken your position.

ARNOLD   They're all downstairs. You'd better go.

MISS SYMPATHY *(Starting away)*   You do understand?

ARNOLD *(Dryly)*   I think I hear planes.
(She exits running. Sound of offstage pounding.)

BARRY *(Offstage)*   Goddamit, Millie! What are you doing in there? Unlock the door!
(Sound of pounding)

GRACE *(Offstage)*   That's not nice, Millie! Let us into our fallout shelter!
(Sound of pounding)

BARRY *(Offstage)*   Millie! There is such a thing as the laws of trespass! You're in *my* shelter!
(Sound of pounding. MISS SYMPATHY *enters)*

ARNOLD *(Grinning)*   Millie locked herself in the shelter?

MISS SYMPATHY   She says, "Let the white imperialists wipe each other out." *(*ARNOLD *laughs)* I can appreciate her sensitivity and support her aspirations but I reject the extremes to which she's gone. *(Brightly)*   But I do understand her motivations.
(Sound of pounding)

BARRY *(Offstage)*   Millie, you're not playing fair!

ARNOLD   You really shouldn't be up here, you know.

MISS SYMPATHY   I thought we were having an all clear by default.

ARNOLD   I doubt it.

BARRY *(Offstage)*   All right, Millie. We'll stay down here anyway! We'll use the basement as our shelter! Down on your stomach, Grace. Where's Miss Sympathy? Miss Sympathy!

MISS SYMPATHY *(Yelling)*   Upstairs! I thought it was over!

BARRY *(Offstage)*   The law's the law, Miss Sympathy. We can't come up till we hear the all clear. Otherwise we'd be making Khrushchev happy!

ARNOLD   It *is* the law.

MISS SYMPATHY   What if I lay on my stomach up here? It's so dusty down there.

ARNOLD   I guess that would be *semi*-compliance.

MISS SYMPATHY   Does it seem within the spirit of the law to you?

ARNOLD   Well, I know lying on your stomach *is* the accepted crisis position. I don't imagine you'd be penalized because of location. *(She lies on her stomach.* ARNOLD *views her with wry amusement)* Don't you know how to stand?

MISS SYMPATHY *(Dryly)*   That's quite witty. You were telling me about your fantasy.

ARNOLD   Which one?

MISS SYMPATHY   Your uncle.

(Checks notes)   Walter.

ARNOLD   Well, in a fantasy it's you who are in control, isn't it? So you can make things any way you want them. So I wanted an uncle. I guess I was eight or nine at the time. So I made him up. Uncle Walter. Uncle Walter was a mess. His eyes were very bad and he wore big, thick bifocals—about this size—half the size of his face and he had a beard. Hair all over. I mean it started with his nose hairs and blended with his ear hairs and went all the way down to his chest hairs. Except I never saw his chest. He was frail and he always wore a scarf. And a big heavy black overcoat. Even inside the house. It used to shed. *He* used to shed. My mother and father were always embarrassed when he came to visit. And I was too— but for *them*, not for him. I kept hoping Uncle Walter would understand that I was as normal as he was and that it wasn't my fault my parents were a little strange. He would never let me near him. He *hated* children. So *I* hated children. Anything Uncle Walter did I wanted to do. I tried to get bad eyes. I'd let them blur out of focus until they'd tear. I began seeing my parents as Uncle Walter saw them. I don't mean I began to understand them the way Uncle Walter did. I mean I *became* Uncle Walter looking at my parents. I became Uncle Walter looking at *me!* Then—I don't know how it happened—my father talked Uncle Walter into joining his athletic club. I thought it was a big joke—that in a week Uncle Walter would have them all wearing overcoats, bifocals and beards—
(Mimes sign) "The Unhealthy Athletic Club." But all that happened was that Uncle Walter got healthy. He got rid of his overcoat. He shaved his beard. He took pills for his vitamin deficiency and his eyes became twenty-twenty. He began to smile at me and say, "Howsa boy!" He talked business with the family. It was *my* fantasy and he had sold me out! He died a month later. Never trust a grownup.

MISS SYMPATHY   Will you tell me why you're crawling?
(Arnold crawls over to MISS SYMPATHY*)*

ARNOLD   I find that in crawling like a child I begin to act like a child again.

MISS SYMPATHY   Is that why you started?

ARNOLD   Possibly. I did a very childlike thing on the way home. I never would have thought of doing such a thing before I crawled. As an adult my values encompassed a rigid good, a rigid evil and a mushy everything in between. As a child I've rediscovered one value I had completely forgotten existed.

MISS SYMPATHY   What's that?

ARNOLD   Being naughty.

MISS SYMPATHY   You did something naughty on the way home. Is that what you're telling me?

ARNOLD   I don't think I want to talk about it right now. I want to enjoy it by myself for a little while longer.

MISS SYMPATHY *(Exasperated)*   God, you're as hard to reach as a child!
(Quickly)   I understand why, of course.

ARNOLD   Why?

MISS SYMPATHY   First you tell me what you did today that was naughty.

ARNOLD   First you tell me why I'm as hard to reach as a child.

MISS SYMPATHY *(As if to a child)*   First you tell me what you did that was naughty.

ARNOLD *(Kidding)*   You first.

MISS SYMPATHY *(As if to a child)*   Oh no, you!

ARNOLD *(Kidding)*   I asked you first.

MISS SYMPATHY *(As if to a child)*   Then will you tell me?

ARNOLD *(Trying to withdraw)*   Yes.

MISS SYMPATHY *(Very arch)*   Promise?

ARNOLD *(Serious)*   Yes.

MISS SYMPATHY *(Very arch)*   Cross your heart and hope to die?

ARNOLD *(Stares at her, unbelieving)*   I can understand why you have trouble reaching children.

BARRY *(Offstage)*   Hey, up there. Have you heard the all clear sound yet?

MISS SYMPATHY *(Yelling angrily)*   No, it hasn't, Mr. Enterprise!

BARRY *(Offstage)*   Funny. It should have sounded by now.

GRACE *(Offstage)*   I'm getting a chill lying on my stomach this way.

BARRY *(Offstage)*   It's the proper position, Grace.

GRACE *(Offstage)*   Can't we go up soon, Barry?

BARRY *(Offstage)*   When the all clear sounds we'll go up. That's the law. Is that Millie yelling something?

GRACE *(Offstage)*   Yell louder, Millie. We can't hear you—*(Pause)*   She wants to know if the all clear sounded yet.

BARRY *(Offstage)*   Tell her to go to hell.

ARNOLD *(After a long study of* MISS SYMPATHY*)*   Do you really want me to get up?

MISS SYMPATHY *(Petulantly)*   It's not what *I* want. It's what's best for yourself.

ARNOLD   You mean if I got up I'd be doing it for myself.

MISS SYMPATHY *(Petulantly)*   Not for me. Not for your mother. Not for your father. Strictly for yourself.

ARNOLD   That's too bad. I don't care much about getting up for myself. I would have liked to have done it for you though.

MISS SYMPATHY *(With sudden warmth)*   I *would* be very pleased.

ARNOLD   If I got up right now?

MISS SYMPATHY *(Warmly)*   Yes.

ARNOLD *(Begins to rise)*   Okay.

MISS SYMPATHY *(Tackles him)*   No!

ARNOLD   But you said—

MISS SYMPATHY   Not *now. Later! (Whispers)*   It's against the law!

ARNOLD *(Shrugs. Returns to his crawling position)*   Did you see my coloring book?

MISS SYMPATHY *(Furious)*   You're not being *honest!* You blame me for accepting the rules of society. Well, without those rules we'd have anarchy. Every mature person has to operate within the warp and woof of society. You want to operate outside that warp and woof, to return to a *child's* world—to start all over again!

ARNOLD (*Appreciatively*)   Yeah!
(*From his pocket he plucks a lollipop*)

MISS SYMPATHY (*Impatiently*)   Well, you *can't* start all over again. It will all come out the same way!

ARNOLD (*Sucking the lollipop*)   Then I'll start all over again.

MISS SYMPATHY   But it will all come out the same way *again*!

ARNOLD   Then I'll start all over again, again, again. It's *my* game.
(*He takes a long, loud suck on the lollipop*)

BARRY (*Offstage*)   Wasn't that the all clear?

MISS SYMPATHY   I'm afraid not, Mr. Enterprise.

GRACE (*Offstage*)   I'm catching cold.

BARRY (*Offstage*)   Let me put my jacket under you.

GRACE (*Offstage*)   I'm *tired* of this.

BARRY (*Offstage*)   But it's only a few minutes. We've spent over two weeks in our shelter.

GRACE (*Offstage*)   But we had television.

BARRY (*Offstage*)   The law is there for the citizens to obey. If *we* are irresponsible how can we attack *others* for being irresponsible?

MISS SYMPATHY (*Coldly, to* ARNOLD)   You have a very irresponsible attitude.

ARNOLD   Naughty is the word I prefer.

MISS SYMPATHY   You were going to tell me something.

ARNOLD   I forgot.

MISS SYMPATHY   What you did on the way home from work—(*With sarcasm*)   Something naughty.

ARNOLD   Do you find me attractive, Miss Sympathy?

MISS SYMPATHY (*A long pause. She begins to sniffle*)   Yes, I do.

ARNOLD (*Surprised*)   You can say it just like that?

MISS SYMPATHY (*Barely restraining tears*)   Because I do. I know I do. You're the kind of person I find attractive *always*. From previous examples I know you fall into my spectrum of attractiveness. Actually, it's because I find you so attractive that I'm having trouble with you. If I didn't find you attractive I could explain your problem without the slightest difficulty.

ARNOLD   Everything's so complicated.

MISS SYMPATHY   We live in a complex world.

ARNOLD   *Children* are complex. Adults are just complicated.

MISS SYMPATHY   Why did you ask if I found you attractive?

ARNOLD   Because we've been alone for a while and we'll be alone for a while longer. I thought it was the right thing to say.

MISS SYMPATHY   We have a time limit. The all clear will probably sound any minute.

ARNOLD   Four months ago you wouldn't have found me attractive.

MISS SYMPATHY   Why do you say that?

ARNOLD   Because four months ago I didn't crawl. Crawling has made me a more attractive person.

MISS SYMPATHY   It has? How?

ARNOLD   Well, for one thing I'm conspicuous now. I never used to be. There's a certain magnetism conspicuous men have for women. *(More cautiously)*   I *think* conspicuous men have for women.

MISS SYMPATHY   No, don't stop. In some ways you're right.

ARNOLD   I'm more assertive now. Everybody used to have *their* road. My mother, my father, my friends, Millie—with me the question was whose road would I take? Whose side was I on? Now I have *my* road, *my* side.

MISS SYMPATHY   You're terribly sweet. Do you mind if I crawl over to you?

ARNOLD   I'd like it. *(She does. For a while they stare wistfully at each other. Then* ARNOLD *drops to his stomach and kisses her)*   I'm on my stomach now.

MISS SYMPATHY   Yes.

ARNOLD   I'm not even crawling any more. That's *real* regression.

MISS SYMPATHY   Yes. *(He kisses her)*   Before we do anything I want to tell you—

ARNOLD   What?

MISS SYMPATHY   Before—when I was feeling sorry for you—I felt you'd rejoin society if you were only made to feel like a man.

ARNOLD   An expert analysis.

MISS SYMPATHY   I was going to offer to go to bed with you to make you feel like a man. I couldn't offer myself in that spirit now.

ARNOLD   I'm glad you told me. The social worker my folks had in last month went to bed with me because she wanted to make me feel like a man. I think she got more out of it than I did.

MISS SYMPATHY   How many have there been?

ARNOLD   One a month for four months. My parents keep bringing them around. They're very nervous about me.

MISS SYMPATHY *(Doubtfully)*   You're not just using me, Arnold—

ARNOLD   We're using each other, Miss Sympathy. That's what using's for.
(He begins to unbutton the back of her blouse)

MISS SYMPATHY   The all clear—What if the all clear should sound?

ARNOLD   It won't. It's broken. That's what I did that was naughty today.
(They embrace as lights dim)

BARRY *(Offstage)*   Was that the all clear?
Curtain

The Relationship

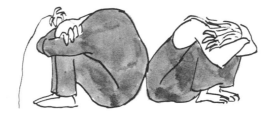

About the Author

Jules Feiffer's cartoons first gained attention seven years ago in the Greenwich Village weekly—*The Village Voice*. Today his syndicated cartoon "Feiffer" appears in fifty newspapers in the United States and some dozen newspapers and magazines abroad—including *The London Observer* and *The Paris Herald-Tribune*. His books have been translated into six languages.

Mr. Feiffer appears regularly in *Playboy* and has appeared in *Harper's*, *Horizon*, *Mademoiselle* and *Holiday*, as well.

His books include *Sick, Sick, Sick, Passionella, The Explainers, Boy, Girl. Boy, Girl., Hold Me!*, and earlier this year, *Harry, the Rat with Women*, a novel. His animated cartoon, *Munro*, won an Academy Award in 1961.

Mr. Feiffer is the winner of a special George Polk Memorial Award in Journalism. He is married and lives in Brooklyn.